JOSEPH HAYDN

QUARTET

for 2 Violins, Viola and Violoncello
B♭ major/B-Dur/Si♭ majeur
Hob.III:78
(Op. 76/4)

Ernst Eulenburg Ltd
London · Mainz · Madrid · New York · Paris · Prague · Tokyo · Toronto · Zürich

I. Allegro con spirito. 1

II. Adagio 12

III. MENUETTO. Allegro 16

IV. FINALE. Allegro, ma non troppo 20

All rights reserved. No part of this publication may be reproduced, stored in a retrieval system, or transmitted in any form or by any means, electronic, mechanical, photocopying, recording or otherwise, without the prior written permission of Ernst Eulenburg Ltd., 48 Great Marlborough Street, London W1V 2BN.

Quartet N.º 78

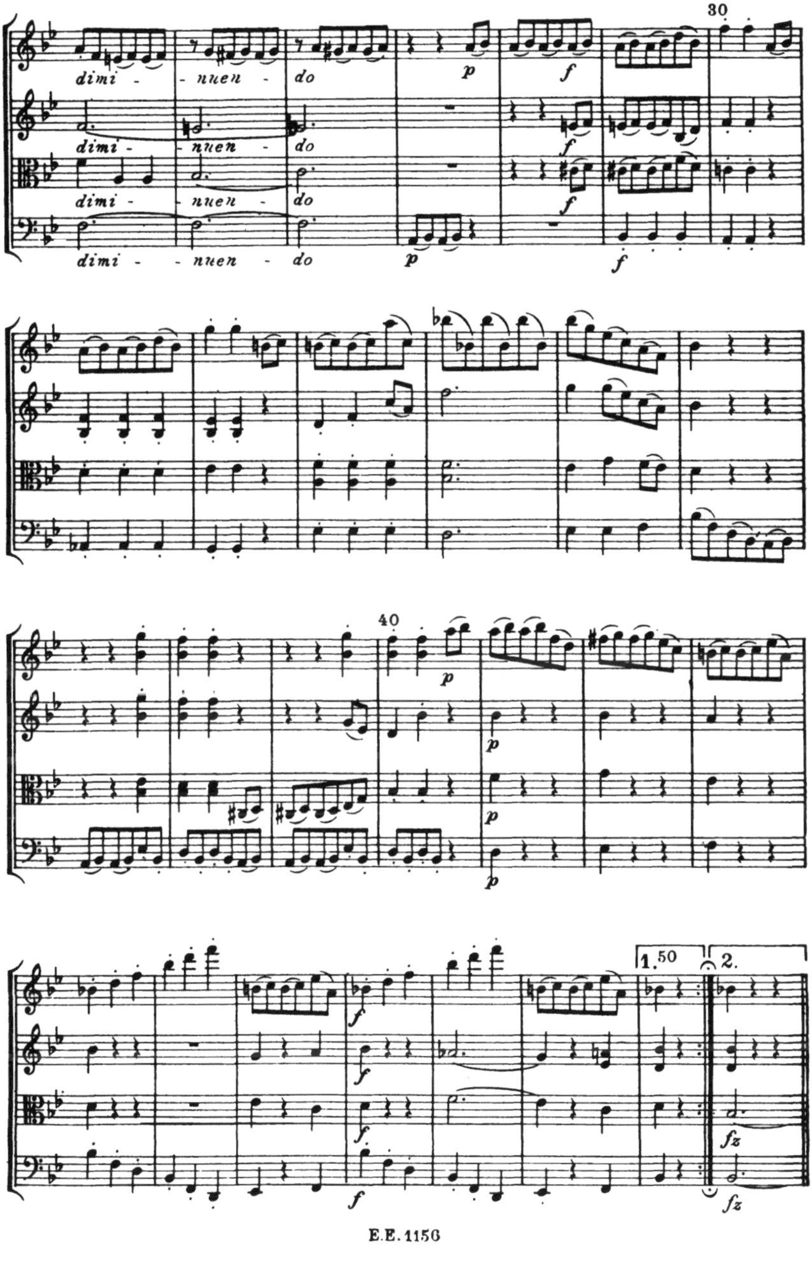
30
dimi - nuen - do
dimi - nuen - do
dimi - nuen - do
dimi - nuen - do
p
f
40
p
f
1. 50
2.
fz

IV